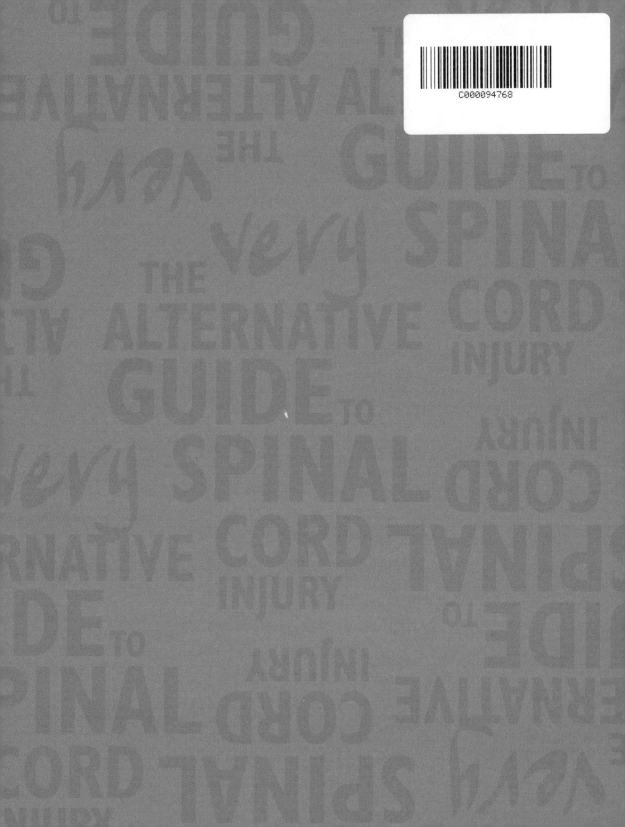

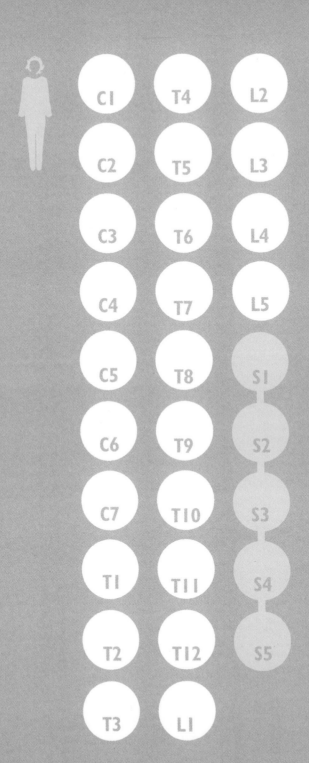

THE *very* ALTERNATIVE GUIDE TO SPINAL CORD INJURY

NAH, IT'S SOME BOOK ON SPINAL INJURY

INTRO

The Very Alternative Guide to Spinal Cord Injury is a partnership between a psychologist and an artist who both wished to produce something a bit different: a witty and fully illustrated guide for those adjusting to the exciting new experience of spinal injury. Joe, the artist, has drawn on his own thrilling experiences of life with a spinal cord injury. Anthony, the psychologist, has drawn upon hours and hours of biscuit-fuelled interviews with spinal cord injured people.

Our aim is to help spinal injured people, their families and their friends. Health professionals may also be interested as the pictures are far more colourful than most boring medical books.

We've noticed that spinal cord injured people often develop a slightly twisted sense of humour. Humour can cut through the fluffy stuff and help people to talk about taboos like toilets, sex, and doctors sticking things where the sun does not shine.

The book is light-hearted in tone, but it is not supposed to be a laugh-a-minute, chuckle-fest. Like spinal cord injury, some bits aren't funny at all. Like spinal cord injury, some bits are downright hilarious.

A book like this cannot be all-things to all-people but we are sure that there is something for most people in the wonderfully varied pages that follow. Even if you find just one little thing to be of benefit, it will make us feel a whole lot better about the extortionate cover price.

Anthony Papathomas & Joe Robinson

IF YOU'RE READING THIS BOOK THERE'S A GOOD CHANCE YOU (OR SOMEONE YOU KNOW) FEELS A BIT LIKE THIS...

ONCE UPON A TIME

How this book starts is down to your inidividual story. While every spinal injury is unique, its immediate physical or emotional impact often sounds the same...

OH *@#%*!

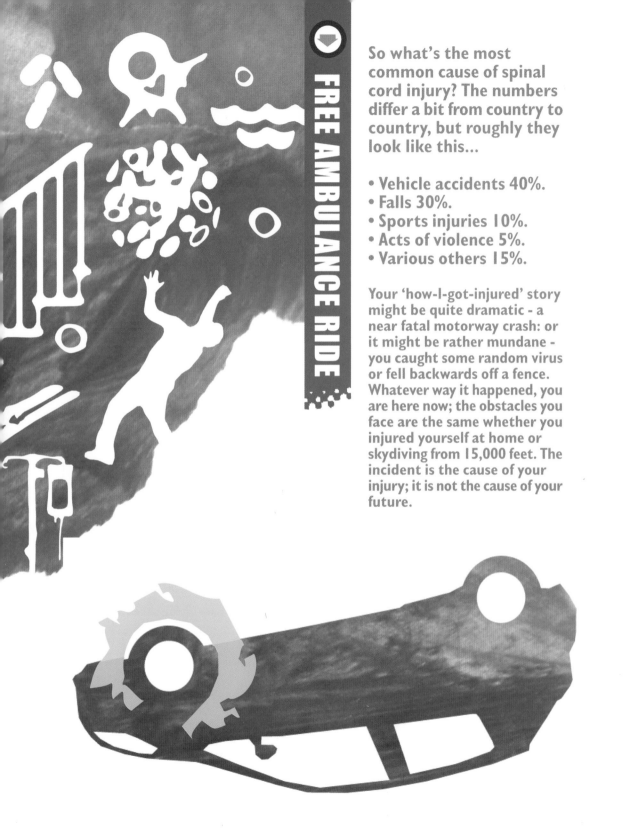

So what's the most common cause of spinal cord injury? The numbers differ a bit from country to country, but roughly they look like this...

• Vehicle accidents 40%.
• Falls 30%.
• Sports injuries 10%.
• Acts of violence 5%.
• Various others 15%.

Your 'how-I-got-injured' story might be quite dramatic - a near fatal motorway crash: or it might be rather mundane - you caught some random virus or fell backwards off a fence. Whatever way it happened, you are here now; the obstacles you face are the same whether you injured yourself at home or skydiving from 15,000 feet. The incident is the cause of your injury; it is not the cause of your future.

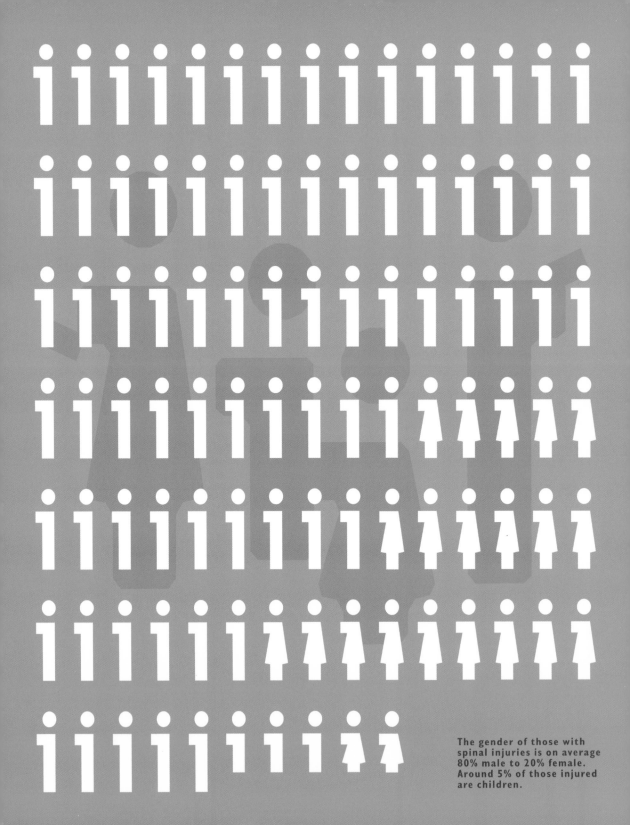

The gender of those with spinal injuries is on average 80% male to 20% female. Around 5% of those injured are children.

ANYONE CAN JOIN

Annually approx

x 1000
New Members

Annually up to

x 500,000
New Members

Worldwide, spinal cord injury is becoming more and more common. Doctors are getting better at treating us in the hours after an accident, so we are less likely to croak it. People who perhaps would have died fifty years ago are now busy wheeling around doing a whole host of fun stuff.

The Spinal Injury Club is definitely expanding and it's open to all - men and women, black and white, old and young. So you aren't quite as unique as you think you are - or in other words, you're not alone.

Present this card at all good shops, restaurants and hotels and watch people's very confused faces.

Valid throughout the world

Executive Member

sci

MY SPINAL CORD INJURY

MEMBERSHIP
CARD

Member since

THE HAND YOU'RE DEALT

HEAD

NECK

YOU

CHEST

TUMMY

BACK

BITS

BUM

CERVICAL
- C1
- C2
- C3
- C4
- C5
- C6
- C7

THORACIC
- T1
- T2
- T3
- T4
- T5
- T6
- T7
- T8
- T9
- T10
- T11
- T12

LUMBAR
- L1
- L2
- L3
- L4
- L5

SACRUM
- S1
- S2
- S3
- S4
- S5

It won't be long before you possess an encyclopaedic knowledge of the various types of spinal cord injury. You'll be so clued up that you'll be wondering why you hadn't considered a career as a surgeon before now.

Your 'level of injury' refers to the exact place in your back that your spinal cord was damaged (see our hi-tech diagram). Usually, higher levels of injury have a bigger impact than lower levels. C-level injuries are associated with tetraplegia - so arms are affected as well as legs; whereas T-Level injuries and below are associated with paraplegia - it's your legs that don't work.

Why not bemuse medical staff by describing your injury as A4 (envelope) M6 (motorway) F16 (jet fighter) or 34B (bra size)?

If the injury is 'complete' there is usually no movement below the level of injury. If the injury is 'incomplete' then there might be some movement below the injury or perhaps a bit of feeling preserved. These categories aren't perfect and just because you and the poor sod in the next bed are both 'L5 incomplete' it does not mean you will have the exact same experience. Whichever hand you have been dealt, the key is to play it well.

MOST LIKELY

YOU'RE GOING TO FEEL COMPLETELY...

Vb-1686 (slang)(skrūd) beset with negative circumstances that appear difficult or impossible to overcome

Ok, so you feel screwed? That's because you're cutting away at your future with a pair of imaginary scissors - 'I won't work again', 'I'll never be out with my friends', 'I can't go back home…'

SNIP, SNIP, SNIP

Each cut of the scissors leaves you with less and less until eventually there is nothing left. Guess what? You feel screwed.

Throw the scissors away. It's hard not knowing what the future holds but a broken back doesn't mean everything is over. Don't second-guess the rest of your life, it's early days.

You should also pack away that emotional suitcase marked 'what if?' You don't need that kind of baggage. It's pointless being haunted by events you can't change. You are where you are and the only suitcase you need is the one for your underwear and your duty free.

BEEN THERE, GOT THE T-SHIRT

After a traumatic event like a spinal cord injury, most people will spend time wearing some, or all, of these t-shirts. This is a natural and very personal process - there is no timetable or right way to do it. Some people change their t-shirt by the hour; others wear the same t-shirt for days, weeks, or even months. So, what colour t-shirt are you wearing today?

Machine wash
Only non-chl
Do

'This isn't happening. It can't be true'

Hearing 'you'll never walk again' is a tough pill to swallow. Denial is a normal reaction to any traumatic life change. Avoiding the issue might help short-term, but sooner or later facing up to the reality of what has happened is the way to go. As soon as you do, you've taken a giant step forward (so to speak).

'If I'm able to walk again I'll change my life. I'll be a better person, I promise'

You might try and make a deal with yourself, with life, or even with God. Suddenly all you have to do to get better is be nicer to others and think flowery thoughts forever and ever. The main problem is that it doesn't work, but then you probably knew that. The best kind of bargaining is rewarding yourself when you achieve a goal - 'If I work hard at physio, I'm treating myself to that DVD Boxset'.

COLLECT THE SET
(OR JUST PICK
THE ONES YOU
FEEL LIKE)

☐ DENIAL
☐ BARGAINING
☐ ANGER

☐ ACCEPTANCE
☐ DEPRESSION
☐ OTHER

'Spinal injury units can be angry places full of angry people'

As reality dawns you will probably be a bit pissed off with everything and everyone. Shouting and swearing can be a release, but it might also make you feel a bit guilty. Don't stress yourself out - you're going through a lot and everyone knows that. Soon enough the vase of flowers you threw at the wall will be something you can all look back at and laugh.

ANGER RRR

DEPRESS ION

'There are bad nights where tears come - depression is a common reaction I think. I know for a fact everybody goes through a bad place'

It's hard to stay positive with all the stuff that is going on. There are times when you will feel very down. It can be comforting to know that pretty much everyone feels this way, and pretty much everyone gets through it. Sometimes all you will need is a hug and it is not uncool to ask for one.

'I stopped focusing on just bad stuff and I started thinking about the future, getting home, even back to work'

Bit by bit the process of coming to terms with your injury is taking place. Now you feel like you are starting to get it together and also looking forward more than looking back. You get some measure of what has happened and you are starting to make decisions with clarity - what are you going to do with rest of your life? This is a good t-shirt to hang on to.

ACCEPTANCE

S/M/L/XL/XXL

A BRAVE FACE

It's been said that one of the most difficult tasks for a spinal injured person is to 'cheer up' their visitors! Worrying about the sadness caused to friends and family can be a real stress.

You might feel the need to put on a brave face, but doing this can be exhausting at a time when you need all the energy you can get. Reassure others if you can; but don't feel guilty if you can't.

If you are on the other side of the bed it will hurt to see someone you care about go through a spinal injury. But life is not over, it's just taken a dramatically unexpected direction. You can help each other steer a new course.

ONE TO ONE

In the period following your injury, you and your loved ones may not know what to say to each other.

This is a scary time. Most of us avoid sensitive questions yet you've probably got hundreds you want to ask.

The sooner you can talk about this stuff, the better. So when you feel ready...

* Please seek medical advice if you are craving a pizza or hankering for a double tandoori chicken kebab.

How much recovery will there be?

Is our life over?

What about my job?

Can we get pizza delivered here?*

KIDS

Children often cope with all this tough stuff better than adults; as family members or as patients. They will take their cue from adults though, so it's a good idea to try and keep it together when they're around. It's also important to let young people know that it's okay to ask questions. Questions about anything. Do your best to answer but if you don't know, it's okay to say so.

Kids have a great knack of bringing everyone back to the real world. They move on very quickly and their pet goldfish dying may be more traumatic than any spinal injury.

I'M BORED!

Most hospitals have a machine that goes 'beep'. Ask to see and hear one.

I'M BORED!

A handy drawing book and some crayons or pens can be worth their weight in gold.

Sometimes we forget the young members of the Spinal Injury Club. Roughly 5% of injuries happen to children and emotions can run higher in these circumstances. Because they are still growing, kids will often have to see a variety of additional doctors and specialists. Oh, and they still get schoolwork in hospital!

I'M BORED!

Cut out this fish and stick it on a saline bottle or catheter bag to surprise the nurse.*

* One of the authors actually did this while in hospital and it was very funny.

CERVICAL
DORSAL
SACRAL
CAUDAL

10
13
5
40

Did you know? Other animals have a similar layout of bones to a person.

HEAD

NECK

BACK

CHEST

TUMMY

BITS

BUM

The Tyrannosaurus Rex did have slightly sharper teeth and a longer tail.

Can you draw a dinosaur skeleton?

BORED

It's hard to imagine how excruciatingly bored you can get. Stuck for weeks, hardly able to move, staring up at the ceiling. You find yourself eagerly awaiting exciting events like lunch, dinner or having your blood pressure taken. Television and visitors can help, but there's no way around it; there'll be moments when you're so bored you'll feel like screaming.

It's one of life's cruellest mysteries. In every ceiling, in every hospital, there is always at least one wonky tile. It will drive you round the bend.

FIZZIOTHERAPY

There's a fair chance you'll develop a love-hate relationship with your physiotherapist. These smiling assassins come with a mischievous plan. With faces like angels they will treat you like a puppet; pushing, pulling, bending. It will take you to your limit and just when you're about to collapse you'll hear these immortal words - 'it's for your own good'. What's worse, they're right.

LOVE

HATE

TRY READING THIS UPSIDE DOWN DURING PHYSIO

As exhausting as it can be; physiotherapy is essential to getting the most out of what your body can still do. Throwing yourself into your physio sessions is a great idea. Make sure you get the sessions you're entitled to - and take extra ones if you can. A physiotherapist can end up feeling a bit like a best friend - they'll encourage, cheer and motivate you. Get stuck in.

The trusty sidekick to the physiotherapist is the occupational therapist. 'OTs' as they are known will help you adapt to your daily living and work environment. They'll teach you things like how to get in and out of your chair, your car, your bath, your bed. A whole host of other important stuff too. Again, get stuck in.

NB: Despite their title, occupational therapists don't provide careers advice.

"Physiotherapy was hard and at times it felt like I was getting very little back from all the effort. But I was making some progress certainly. The one thing you find is it's very, very slow"

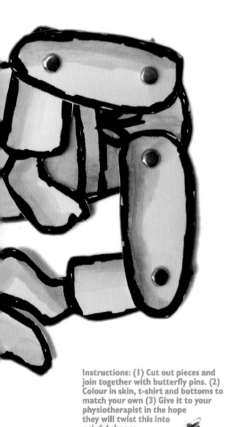

Instructions: (1) Cut out pieces and join together with butterfly pins. (2) Colour in skin, t-shirt and bottoms to match your own (3) Give it to your physiotherapist in the hope they will twist this into painful shapes rather than you.

COLOUR IN TO MATCH YOU

OPTIONAL HAIR STYLES

CUT OUT & COLOUR IN

OOPS I DID IT AGAIN

One of the worst parts of the spinal injury rollercoaster is discovering that the bowel and bladder control button has been switched 'off'. It's pretty crappy; both emotionally and, at first, literally.

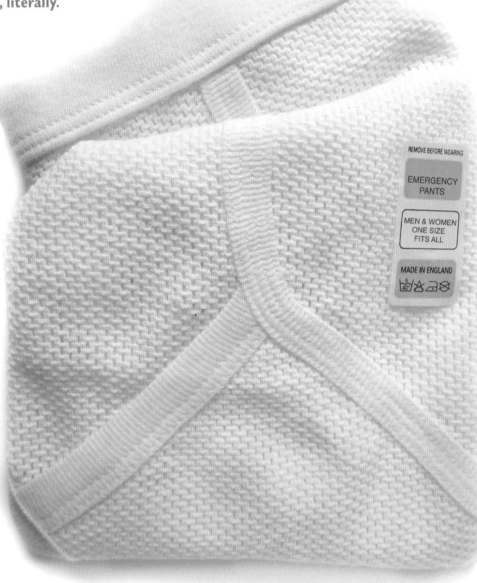

REMOVE BEFORE WEARING

EMERGENCY
PANTS

MEN & WOMEN
ONE SIZE
FITS ALL

MADE IN ENGLAND

**EMERGENCY PANTS
SITUATION**

Available in white or standard British brown

"I can smile about it now but at the time it just smashed me to pieces - it absolutely smashed me to pieces"

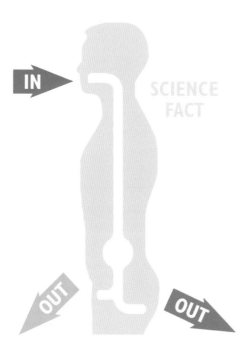

IN

SCIENCE FACT

OUT

OUT

1. **WALNUTS** ■

2. **NUGGET BAR** ■

3. **CRACKED SAUSAGE** ■

4. **SMOOTH SAUSAGE** ■

5. **SOFT NEAT BLOBS** ■

6. **MUSHY PEAS** ■

7. **SOUP** ■

You can collect the set but we recommend aiming for 3,4 and 5

To avoid bladder problems being more of a bummer than they already are; there are two big bits of advice.

1: Eating or drinking less than you should, actually makes things worse. A balanced intake will support a balanced exit.

2: A happy bladder is crucial. So washing hands and keeping things clean downstairs will reduce the chance of infections. Bladder infections can have some seriously bad side effects - so keep a close eye on it.

Everyone is affected differently, but there are some things true for all...

● It's embarrassing.

● You WILL learn to deal with it.

● There will be accidents.

● A spare pair of pants in the hand is worth two in the nearest shop.

● Urologists are always keen to shove things up you.

TIME

In the early days, there are no simple answers to the questions 'how will I cope?' and 'how much recovery will there be?' It can be many months, even years, before you will get full answers. No one, not even your doctors, knows exactly what will happen.

There may be no physical recovery possible at all. If any movement does come back it will take a long time and may fall short of what you were hoping for. Either way it's tough, frustrating and even scary.

You may not realise it at first but you will be making progress. It might not be physical, but it certainly will be emotional progress. Changes are happening; they just take time to notice.

dear diary

Keeping any kind of diary or record can be a good thing to do.

It may not come naturally but it can really help. You can look back at stuff and see how life is moving.

It also gets worries out of your head and frees your brain up for other stuff. Okay, this sounds a bit touchy-feely but it can work. Try it.

If there are issues with physically being able to write then force (sorry persuade) someone to assist you. Tell them it's private and ask them to help you write stuff down.

It doesn't have to be a proper diary. It can be scraps of paper. You can write, make lists, doodle, text, blog, email. Start it for you alone. If you want to tell the world later that's cool.

USE WHEN READY

It happens constantly. First thing in the morning and last thing at night. Whether by phone, text, or in person, the question is always the same: 'How are you?' Yes it's only because people care but it can get a bit annoying after a while. You might get asked twenty times a day and it can be stressful thinking of something new to say. Stress no more as we've solved this particular problem for you.
If anyone asks, just hold up this page.

HOLD HERE

Take a photo of yourself holding this sign. Then forward it to anyone who asks you for a progress report.

PRESENT PAGE AS SHOWN

K

HOLD HERE ➤

being honest

There may be moments when you feel like you can't go on.

"Sometimes you feel like you're beyond help. There were times I seriously considered I shouldn't really be here, I cannot do this..."

YES YOU CAN

Right now you're probably focusing on all the stuff you can't do anymore. So we've taken it upon ourselves to list some 'can do's' we've heard from spinal injured people. There are a few spaces to add some things that are personal to you. You could even use them to set some goals for yourself. 'By the end of the year I am going to...'

- ....
- ....
- ....

- Take up a new sport.
- Collect keys to my new car.
- Fall in love again.
- Throw a party.
- Meet new people.
- See my favourite band.
- Go on holiday.
- Start a new business.
- Watch the World Cup.
- Cook for your friends.
- Laugh, hard.
- Watch a beautiful sunset.
- Take my child for a spin in the wheelchair.
- Complete a marathon.
- Have dinner with Kylie Minogue*

*Not achieved as yet but one of the authors wanted to put the idea out there for a certain lady to see.

"For me it's all about attitude; if you want to do it, you'll find a way"

All the quotes in this book are quotes from real people, with real spinal cord injuries.

They are the words of those who have been there. They can tell you what only a spinal injured person can: what it's like.

...etter one after the accident I think,
...with lots of different sides to me. Okay,
...or a period of time after the accident
... was a mess. But now, I don't view
...isability as a crisis. I'm on a different
...ath, and I think a better, more fulfilling
...ne. So I'm happy."

"I've definitely come a long way...

...I feel I'm progressing, not only
individually, but also in my
relationships with other people.
There are many positive things to
come out of being disabled. But
don't get me wrong, life isn't
perfect. Far from it. Certainly
along the way there are a lot of
problems that can force me off
the track. And there are times
when I think, 'Well this week,
you've gone back two steps.'"

"I'm still learning. And I think part of the beauty of life is not knowing what will happen in the future. Life is uncertain."

...I've come to think that
on this journey, yes disability can be a shattering experience
... people. But it shouldn't be. Why?
Because it's an opportunity to explore yourself and become
a better person. Still, that doesn't happen overnight."

...saying that I've changed and becom...
a better person because of everythin...
doesn't mean that I've settled on wh...
I am yet. I haven't said 'I am this
person'. I'm still developing mysel...
and I'm more interested in the typ...

"I've come to think of my body as part of me and I accept
that it doesn't do things that it could in the past. I suppose
as well that I use it differently. In that sense, I've made
... others of course. But,
okay, I've made a lot of progress. But there are a lot of
ups and downs on the journey I'm on. It isn't easy. Still,
I wouldn't change back to how it was before the accident...

becoming.

THE BODY BEAUTIFUL?

In our minds we all have a picture portrait of how we see ourselves. It's based on how we feel about things like our health, our age, and how attractive we think we are.

With a spinal injury, your body image (along with your actual body) takes a hell of a whack. Losing control of your legs, arms and more, can make you feel like you're no longer a whole man or a whole woman.

But the whole you is much more than just your physical body. You are your thoughts, your feelings, and your passions. You are how you treat other people. You are your goals and ambitions. Spinal injury doesn't change any of that.

So, if you were a grumpy, unhappy and thoroughly irritating person before your injury, a wheelchair is not going to change that. Likewise, if you were an optimistic, warm and easy going person, then nothing about a spinal injury will take that away. Even with 50% off, you are still 100% you.

Our friend Lisa here is regarded as one of the most beautiful and fascinating women in history. She is said to have been the wife of a wealthy silk merchant, but nobody really knows and nobody really cares. What they do care about is her smile. It's what's going on in her head and her heart that intrigues people.

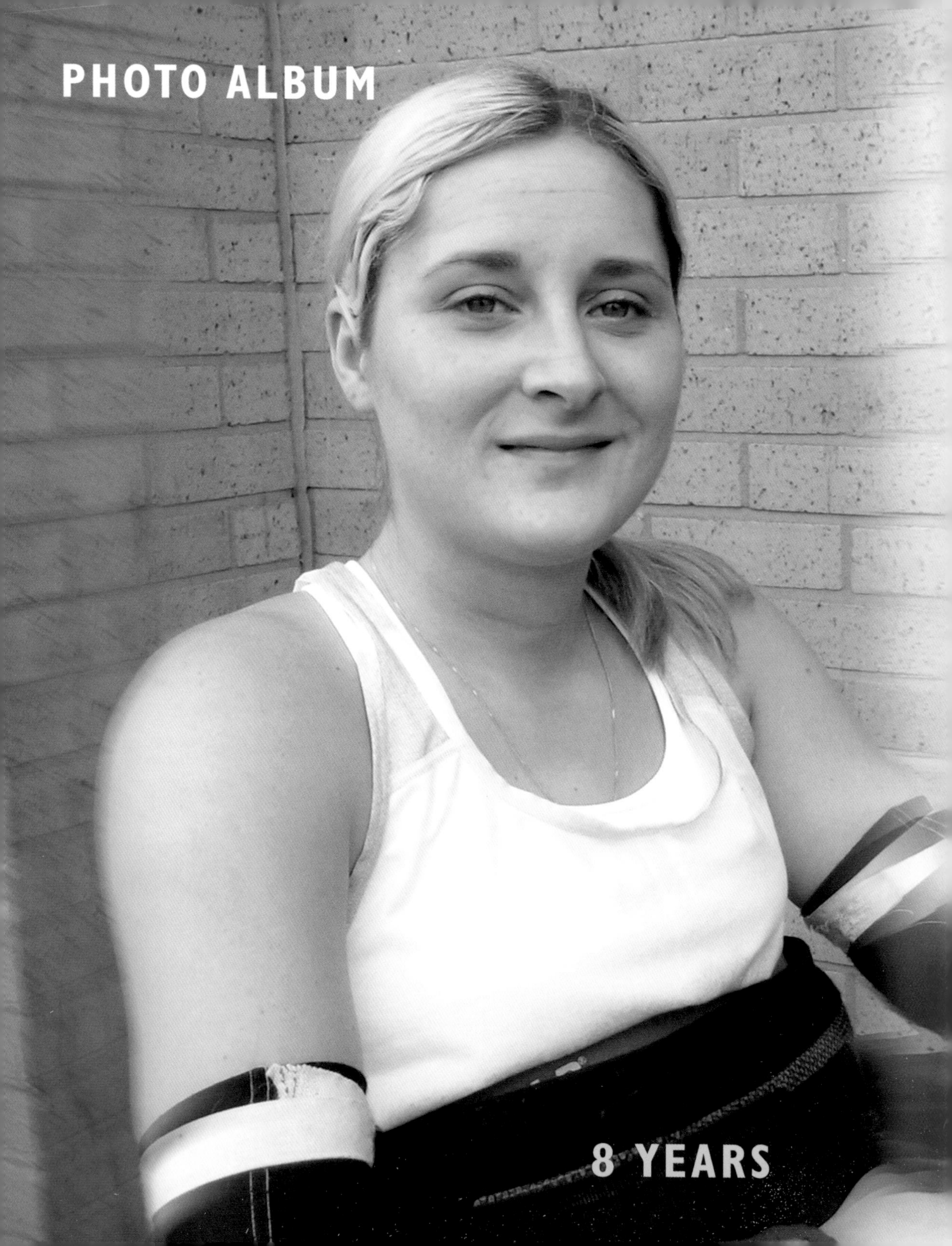
PHOTO ALBUM
8 YEARS

3 YEARS

4 MONTHS

SMALLEST ACCESS RAMP IN WORLD	 40	GREAT BIRTHDAY PARTY. MOVE AHEAD ONE	GET TICKETS TO A GREAT GIG	FIND FUN BO●● CALLED 'VER● ALTERNATIV● GUIDE TO SPIN● CORD INJUR●
HAVE A WEEKEND AWAY	MEET SOME NEW INTERESTING PEOPLE. MOVE AHEAD THREE	WATCH A BEAUTIFUL SUNSET. MOVE AHEAD ONE	 35	NO-BLUE-BAD● CAR IN YOU● SPACE
 19	ANNUAL CHECK-UP ALL OKAY. MOVE AHEAD ONE	 ↑ Outpatients Department 21	22	23
FIRST WEEK BACK AT WORK	MOVE AHEAD ONE SQUARE BUT MISS A GO TO GIVE YOURSELF TIME TO THINK	FIRST HOLIDAY SINCE YOUR INJURY	STILL NO RECOVERY. MOVE AHEAD TWO OR RETURN TO SQUARE THREE	FRIEND GOE● THE EXTR● MILE FOR Y●
	START  1	FINALLY DISCHARGED FROM HOSPITAL	TOTALLY COMMIT TO 100% RECOVE●

SNAKES & RAMPS

A new direction in mission-based gameplay with visually stunning graphics and custom controls for fingers with dice and hand moved counters.

| OU ARE ON UR JOURNEY. OVE AHEAD ONE | 45 | URINARY INFECTION. GO BACK THREE | 47 | 48 YOU WIN |

LAUGH SO UCH YOU WET YOURSELF

DISABILITY BENEFITS HASSLE

FEEL A BIT DOWN ABOUT STUFF. MISS ONE GO

30

YOU COMPLETE A MARATHON. MOVE AHEAD FOUR

PRESSURE ORES. MISS HREE TURNS

PLEASE RING FOR ASSISTANCE
25

26

27

ACTUALLY GET BITTEN BY A SNAKE! BIZARRE. GO BACK ONE

STILL NO EANINGFUL RECOVERY. T ANGRY WITH OCTORS. GO BACK ONE

LIFT OUT OF ORDER AT GYM

EXERCISE GREAT FOR MUSCLE TONE. MOVE AHEAD ONE SQUARE

YOU TAKE UP A WHEELCHAIR SPORT

IF YOUR LIFE IS OVER MISS FIVE TURNS. IF IT'S NOT THEN MOVE BACK TWO

ALL BLADDER CCIDENT OUT SHOPPING

THERE IS NO POINT. EVERYTHING IS CHAOS. GO BACK FOUR

A FRIEND FREAKS OUT AT SEEING YOU IN WHEELCHAIR

GET HELP AND SEE A WAY FORWARD. MOVE AHEAD FIVE SQUARES

GOLDFISH DIES

Now that you have reached this stage of the book we think you need a break. Fancy a game?

Snake

Ramp

LOCATION, LOCATION, LOCATION

One of the horrible consequences of your injury is that your home may no longer be suitable for you to live in. You may even be forced to move.

Finding somewhere to live is hard at the best of times; throw in a life-changing injury and the tough just got a whole lot tougher.

So what are your options? Take a peek in our Estate Agent window and see what's there...

Property: **Partially Adapted**

Location: Where you lived before, your parents place, a rented flat.

Beds: One, possibly unused - you may have to sleep in the living room.

£ Price: Some independence, overall loss of space, general inconvenience.

Description: Moving back to your old place may seem like an ideal scenario but if it **isn't adapted properly** then it may not meet your needs. You will most likely have to compromise on something, which can be frustrating. If you share your house with your family, they will also have to make sacrifices. This arrangement can work, but it can also be a lot of effort for something that isn't quite right.

500mm

250mm

Cat flap

New door

New wall

Property: **Other**

Location: Your existing home with the

Property: **Fully Adapted**

Location: Your own home or a brand new house.

Beds: Minimum two - one for a personal assistant if needed.

£ Price: Worth every penny.

Description: A fully adapted home is a fantastic scenario whether it's **your old home** or a **new home**. You may well miss your old set-up, but it won't take long for you to reap the benefits. You'll soon realise you can do what you want, when you want. Everyday stuff can be done with minimum fuss and effort - leaving time for you to get on with life.

Property: **Care Home**

Location: Often remote, miles away from anyone and anything.

Beds: Lots, usually filled with people you have nothing in common with.

£ Price: Your sense of humour, the will to live, and possibly your sanity.

Description: Care homes may be fine for a brief stop-over while you sort stuff out, but you need to make damned sure you don't get stuck there. Seriously. Facilities aren't properly equipped for spinal injured people.
These sorts of places are typically designed for the elderly - so late night parties are probably a no-no. The fact of the matter is, if you end up in a care home long-term, you are more likely to become isolated and depressed. Fight like blazes to avoid it.

 work

Whether it's your current job or something new, getting back to work is a major challenge (understatement of the year). A lot will depend on your injury and the type of work you do - it will be easier to get back to the office than it will the building site. Either way, there are no real guarantees other than it'll take time (that word again!), perseverance and bulldog spirit to get what you want.

Some people we talked to had already got back on the career ladder. They currently work as...

Magazine Editor
Travel Guide
Writer
Fitness Instructor
Pyschologist
Secretary
Fire Sculptor
Caterer
Life Coach
Nutritionist
IT Consultant
Civil Servant
Charity Worker
Athlete
Designer

Spinal Cord Injury

Very Alternative Guide jobs

find a job jobs by email your jobs search recruiters career advice courses post a job

NEW

Situations Vacant

Newly spinal cord injured individual seeks employment. Would prefer to work in their existing job / with their current employer but assistance required to do so. Help appreciated with any new employment decisions and fulfilling

THE VERY
ALTERNATIVE
GUIDE to
SPINAL
CORD
INJURY

'If someone had supported me I'd have found a way to have done that job again - but no they all just gave up on me'.

'I was very fortunate with my line manager, she was very supportive through it all. I was in hospital for some time, so coming and visiting me and all the rest of it and she said "come back to work"'.

NEW SET OF WHEELS

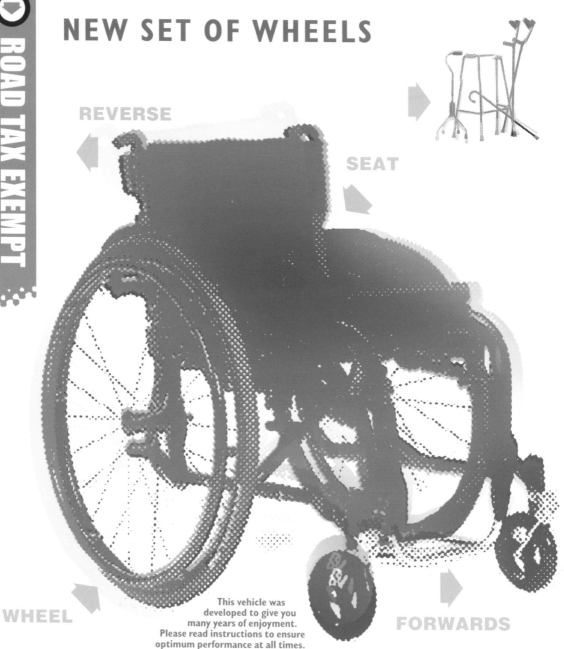

REVERSE

SEAT

WHEEL

This vehicle was
developed to give you
many years of enjoyment.
Please read instructions to ensure
optimum performance at all times.

FORWARDS

INSTRUCTION

OTHER EXCITING CHOICES

"That's when it hit me, being in a chair. Terrible. Everyone was bigger. Children were bigger. It was terrifying. I felt suffocated. No matter which way I tried to move the chair, people kept coming, I couldn't get away... I remember scooting off to a quiet shop and just stopping. I took a breath and went back out. I was a bit of a rally driver for a bit but I was fine soon enough."

Depending on your injury you may be eligible for a host of mobility aids, including the ultimate fashion accessory: a sparkling, shiny new wheelchair. All have optional extras but frustratingly few come with an instruction book. Fitting them into your world can take time but you'll lose your learner plates in good time.

*It has been suggested that this is a very shallow thing to do.

CARERS

A carer - or personal assistant as they should be called - might be necessary. For some, it is more about saving time during the day, for others it's essential to living. We know finding a personal assistant can be a real ordeal; so here are some things to think about...

- They will be a big presence in your life.
- There are good carers and not so good carers.
- You should like them and there has to be trust.
- Don't be scared to change if it's not working.
- Being cared for by a family member can work but it's not always easy.
- It can't work if you feel guilty about asking for your needs to be met.

CHAIR PERK

CHECKING PEOPLE OUT WITHOUT OBVIOUSLY CHECKING THEM OUT*

GROUND CONTROL

As much as you may have once stared at ceilings you'll also become an expert on the ground. Your eagle eyes will soon be trying to spot paving cracks, potholes and how steep the pavement is. It actually becomes second nature soon enough but there'll still be the odd time when you end up privately cursing unthinking architects, planners and council reps. Oh, and dog owners.

① Mud ② Crack ③ Cobble ④ Drop

NOW YOU SEE ME, NOW YOU DON'T

We know it happens, but until you've experienced it first-hand it's hard to imagine how it feels...

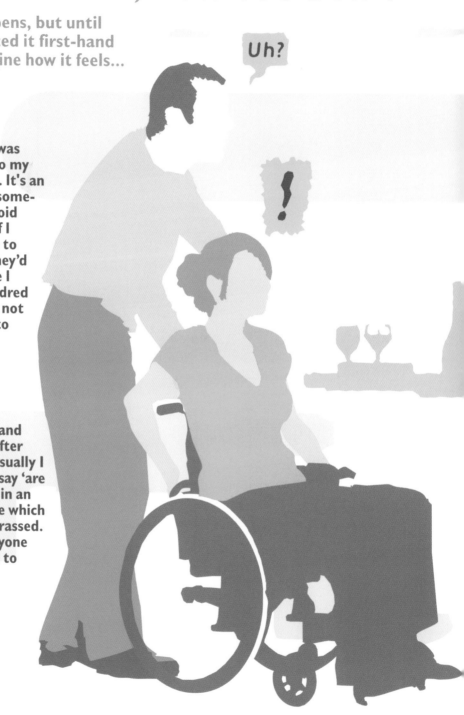

Uh?

!

"One thing I hated was people would talk to my partner and not me. It's an awful feeling when somebody is trying to avoid catching your eye. If I was blessed enough to be acknowledged they'd raise their voice like I was a couple of hundred feet down. It's hard not to feel patronised, to feel angry".

"These situations occur far too often and I still get furious - after nearly fifty years! Usually I just ignore them or say 'are you talking to me?' in an angry and loud voice which makes them embarrassed. And heaven help anyone with me who starts to talk for me!"

HI, WHAT DOES SHE WANT?

PROBLEM

LIMITED FIELD OF VISION

IGNORANCE

RESTRAINED ANGER

SOLUTIONS

RUN OVER THEIR TOES

TRAIN A PARROT
TO TALK TO THEM *

HOLD UP A LARGE
HELPFUL SIGN

* It has been suggested that asking a friend or carer to dress up like a parrot is a useful alternative.

If you're one of the walking spinal injured, you might manage a slow, wobbly walk that is a joy to behold. Not fully paralysed, not fully able-bodied - you're an inbetweener and it can feel like you don't belong anywhere.

Many of the problems faced by inbetweeners are the same as those faced by wheelchair users. The main difference is that your disability isn't as obvious. It's as though support is directed at others, whereas you fade out of view like an old forgotten photograph.

Other members of the Spinal Injury Club might belittle your injury; whereas non-injured people might wonder what all the fuss is about. There are advantages to being a walker, but the idea that you're one of the 'lucky ones' is more than unfair. Just because you can walk in the park doesn't mean it's a walk in the park.

"No one realises that inside you are completely buggered. I can reach a higher shelf in a supermarket and get up a few stairs. But it takes an eternity to do anything and I live in constant panic of falling. I honestly sometimes wish I was in a wheelchair"

Of all the names for the many different types of spinal condition, Cauda Equina syndrome is our favourite. It's right up there with 'anterior inverse cord sequard tabes conus dorsalis medullaris syndrome'.*

Cauda Equina translates as 'horses tail' - which is what the big bunch of nerves in your lower spine look like - the ones that aren't working too well if you have it. If Cauda Equina is your only problem, you might be an inbetweener.

* Okay, so we made this name up.

PAIN

Lots of people don't have any long-term pain at all, but different injuries result in very different experiences. There can be all kinds of pain - muscles, bones, nerves, you name it.

There are no guarantees of ever getting rid of it. But there are ways to stop it overpowering how you live your life.

"Anything I talk about in reference to spinal injury has to reference the pain, because that's been a constant factor and it's never been something that I've been able to totally control"

So how can you reduce pain? Well thinking about sex can help (honestly) and exercise is good too. Both work as a distraction. Some people find relief in relaxation routines and also hypnosis. It's a case of trying out options and seeing if any work for you. Other treatments can include medication but we would recommend avoiding unprescribed drugs or alcohol - however tempting they might be.

TAKE IT SERIOUSLY

When a part of your body is placed under pressure for too long, it can cause serious damage to the skin. The nasty wound that results is known as a pressure sore. Now it's time to get serious.

Imagine the situation... you spend months adjusting physically and mentally, then, just as you get back into the swing of things - wham! A pressure sore sends you back into hospital. A serious case can take months and months to recover from. If that isn't shocking enough, if left untreated, it can kill you.

It's not just pressure that's a problem, friction is too. Something rubbing against your skin can quickly cause a wound. Be aware.

Here are five key points. Sorry, none of them are funny, but they are essential:

- Relieving pressure by shifting your weight is crucial.

- How often you need to shift your weight is individual to you - ask your doctor.

- Know when you're at risk; in your chair all afternoon? On a long journey? In bed with flu? Take extra care.

- Check your body every day for redness in key problem areas.

- Use proper padding and cushioning for things like chair seats, mattresses and pillows.

NOT ALL FACILITIES ARE USER FRIENDLY

WITH DISABLED PARKING BADGES YOU CAN PARK ALMOST ANYWHERE

SKIN

FAT

MUSCLE

BONE

WARNING

Your spinal injury can turn people into interfering buffoons. Here are some examples you may have to deal with...

People jumping in like enthusiastic gazelles to offer their 'help' without even asking if you need assistance. A polite 'no thank you' won't always stop them.

Your wheelchair or walking stick can become part of your personal space. That won't prevent someone trying to have a push, pull or play.

Complete strangers love to ask deeply personal or inappropriate questions: 'Why are you in a wheelchair?' and 'Can you still have sex?' being among the classics.

Nobody wants a round of applause just for popping out to do a bit of shopping - but you can bet it will happen. Prepare to be congratulated on the most basic of tasks - and should you dare to have a night on the town then you might just earn yourself a knighthood.

Well meaning? Yes. Good intentioned? Of course. Very patronising? Most definitely. When face-to-face, some people see the disability before they see you. In some situations patronising can even slide into deeply insulting.

Shopping is also a mixed bag of fun. Some shops have great access and staff and others are just... crap.

Right, so, as we've said, yes you can do loads of fun stuff but all the mundane everyday stuff carries on too. Even things that you might hope to get out of, you can't. Life has changed for you big time, but actually there's loads that hasn't.

Just like everyone else, you can still...

- Pay taxes.
- Lose your wallet.
- Argue with the kids.
- Forget a friend's birthday.
- Pay the rent.
- Attend a dull leaving do.
- Receive a crap present.
- Get a parking ticket.
- Do the laundry.
- Make a prat of yourself.
- Go to the dentist.
- Visit the in-laws.
- Get overcharged for your gas.
- Get *another* unwanted caller.
- Be arrested for drunk and disorderly. *
- ....
- ....
- ....

* Yes, even prison cells can be accessible (so we have been told, neither author has ever been locked up as yet).

YES YOU CAN ALSO

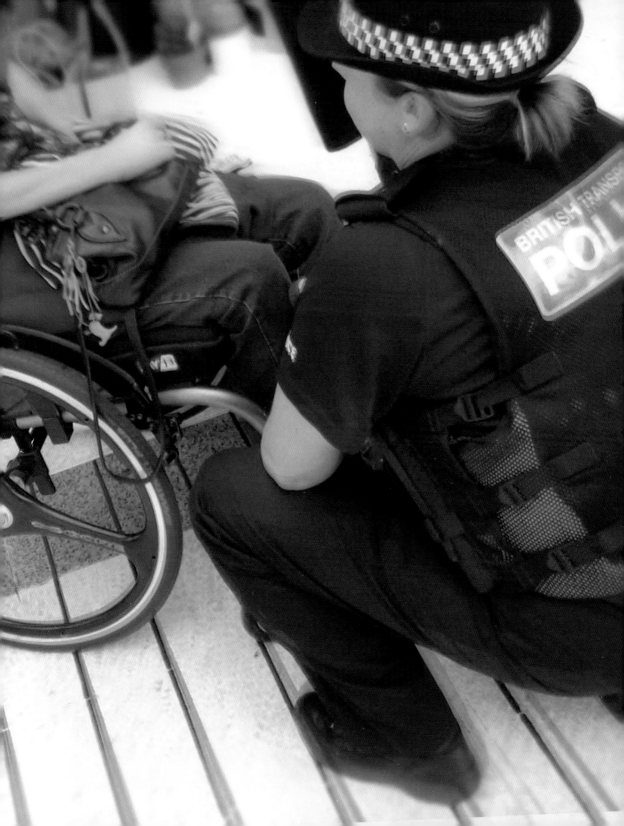

EXERCISE

It's as obvious as a baboon's bum that exercising is a good idea, especially for members of the Spinal Injury Club. There's a lorry load of scientific evidence which says an active lifestyle makes you feel a whole lot better, physically and mentally. Exercise is medicine and it's medicine that works. This 'staying active' business isn't easy though, so here are some moving quotes to inspire you...

"If you do look after yourself you're not going to hospital as much, you're not having any long term problems and hopefully you live longer and healthier"

"ANYONE FOR WHEELCHAIR TENNIS?" SHOUTS GRAN ON HER 80th

EXERCISE

EXERCISE OUTDOORS

"Just being outdoors, just seeing the beauty of where you live, you get the benefit of sunlight on your skin"

EXERCISE PLUS YOU EQUALS FRIENDS

Finding the motivation to exercise can be difficult. Try to do at least 20 minutes of exercise four to five times a week. A mixture of aerobic stuff like walking the dog and strength work like weight machines is the way to go. Try and make it part of your weekly routine and remember: doing something is better than doing nothing.

High level tetraplegics may have fewer options for exercise, but there is still stuff out there - such as adapted archery and even sailing. Give activities a try, they might surprise you.

TREE

TRUNK

NUT

"I like to get into my head that I can take this wheelchair anywhere. So I get loads of ratchet straps, I strap myself into my chair and if I see a tree I'll chuck a strap around a tree and I'll pull myself up the tree. People will walk by and I'm climbing up"

"There's quite a few people who stop and quite enjoy a chat. 'How long have you been doing that?' We've met some really interesting people since I've been hand cycling"

SQUIRREL

Sammy the squirrel says: Exercise sensibly. Too much too soon and you could burn out before you've even started. A physiotherapist can design you a suitable routine.

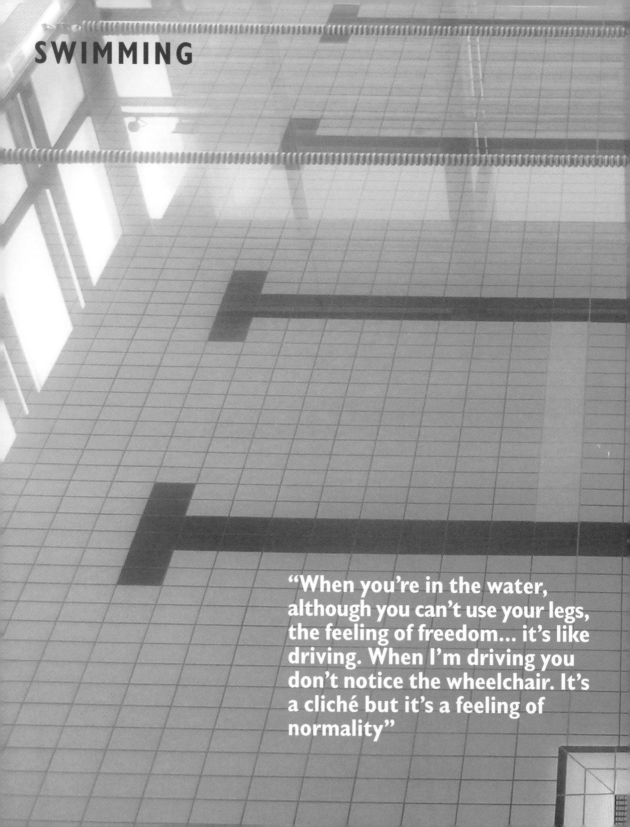

SWIMMING

"When you're in the water, although you can't use your legs, the feeling of freedom... it's like driving. When I'm driving you don't notice the wheelchair. It's a cliché but it's a feeling of normality"

One of the most rewarding ways to do some exercise can be to dip your toe into the calm waters of a local swimming pool. It can engage both your body and mind.

With pools, like all sports and leisure facilities, there can be some troublesome access issues. The faffing around to change can also be a hassle. But if you can find the right place for you, the experience can be great.

"I just find it incredibly relaxing... it just allows me to chill out. I suppose with having a disability one of the nice things about swimming is it's one of the few places you feel able. You've not got the gravity"

NOT ALL FACILITIES ARE USER FRIENDLY

WITH DISABLED PARKING BADGES YOU CAN PARK ALMOST ANYWHERE

SOME ACTIVITIES NEED SPECIALIST EQUIPMENT AND FACILITIES

Sammy the squirrel says: If you take up archery please do it with a proper club and on a proper range.

HORSES FOR COURSES

Spinal injured people can sometimes feel sport is shoved down their throats a bit. If hurtling towards a tattoo-clad, muscle bound wheelchair rugby player doesn't float your boat, there are lots of other things you can do.

A regular trip around the local park can be just as good for you - and you don't even need a tattoo to do it! In short, you don't have to be a Paralympic hopeful to get the most out of exercise.

BAD DAY

Occasionally, when you least expect it, there will be days you feel like crap. It could pain, it could be frustration, it could be bleak thoughts.

Having a

It could be having to deal with some complete idiot.

April

Wk	M	T	W	T	F	S	S
14		1	2	3	4	5	
15	7	8	9	10	11	12	13
16	14	15	16	17	18	19	
17	21	22	23	24	25	26	27
18	28	29	30				

May

Wk	M	T	W	T	F	S	S
					17	18	
		21	22	23	24	25	
		27	28	29	30	31	

June

Wk	M	T	W	T	F	S	S
							1
			6	7			
			13	14	15		
25		18	19	20	21	22	
26	23	24	25	26	27	28	29
27	30						

July

Wk	M	T	W	T	F	S	S
17		1	2	3	4	5	6
18	7	8	9	10	11	12	13
19	14	15	16	17	18	19	20
30	21	22	23	24	25	26	27
31	28	29	30	31			

August

Wk	M	T	W	T	F	S	S
31					1	2	3
32	4	5	6	7	8	9	10
33	11	12	13	14	15	16	17
34	18	19	20	21	22	23	24
35	25	26	27	28	29	30	31

September

Wk	M	T	W	T	F	S	S
36						1	2
37	8	9	10	11	12	13	14

October

Wk	M	T	W	T	F	S	S
40		1	2	3	4	5	6
41	6	7	8	9	10	11	12
42	13	14	15	16	17	18	19

CAN I STILL DO IT? (SEX)

Sex and relationships are complicated. When you're spinal injured, sex and relationships are STILL complicated. But let's cut to the chase - yes you will still want to do it, yes you will still be able to do it, yes other people will still want to do it with you. Our Bonking Bunnies will tell you more...

The biggest single thing to understand is that your sexual experience is going to be different. You are a new you and though sex may not be the same it can be just as good. As you get back to having a sex life, there will be a period of getting comfortable with things as you re-learn about your body.

It might feel a bit like you're discovering sex again for the first time. Going back to those first vulnerable kisses and nervous fumbles. But wasn't that when sex was most exciting?

If you're in a relationship it's really worth getting professional advice as a couple. It might not be easy, but being honest and open is vital. There are experts who can support you.

Find one, grab them, and say 'We wanna talk now!' Speak to someone as soon as you both feel ready. Coming to terms with this in a relationship will be one of the hardest things you will ever do.

Don't forget, there are lots of different ways to be intimate.

The physical stress of a spinal injury may disrupt a woman's monthly cycle. But, sooner rather than later, it should return to normal.

Our thanks to the various birds, bees and educated fleas that gave advice for this rabbit-based page

Whether you're male or female, some things will still be possible and some things will not. Men might find it hard to get hard; whereas women might have limited sensation.

Although sex is usually considered a 'physical act', sexual arousal is very much about the mind. Why is the lingerie industry worth billions? Why do erotic novels sell by the bucket load? Because they both get the mind (and pulse) racing.

There are several medications and aids to help improve these physical elements of sex. Again, get some advice and talk to your partner. You can explore the options together.

The thought of something is as important as the act. Good sex is about your whole body and all your senses. Understand this and you are in for a better time - spinal injured or not.

Spinal cord injury is not a form of family planning contraception. That's right, male and female fertility is not always affected. It's great news, unless your rabbit hutch is already bursting at the seams.

At first, your spinal cord injury might make you feel less attractive. In terms of sexual intimacy, a lack of confidence will hold you back more than your injury will.

The sooner you realise attractiveness is not defined by your disability, the sooner you will be open to a relationship.

Anybody who tells you that a loss of sexual satisfaction is the price you pay for your injury is wrong. In medical terms, they are talking bollocks.

BE MY BABY

The following are all children conceived by someone after they had a spinal cord injury. Just in case you were thinking about it...

Ryan
8lb 9oz
Always hungry

Ayesha
6lb 0oz
Knows what she wants

...or you might be thinking about other things.

Caitlin
7lb 5oz
Dimpled chin

Adam
8lb 6oz
Never sleepy

Jacob
7lb 1oz
Very contented

Leila
7lb 5oz
Loves dressing up

James
7lb 9oz

can I still do it ?

(LOVE)

Yes you can still fall in love. It's as wonderful, painful, confusing and troublsome as it ever was.

Thrifty romantics might think just kissing outside a florist is enough. For a happier date we suggest splashing out on at least one flower.

CHANGE HERE FOR...

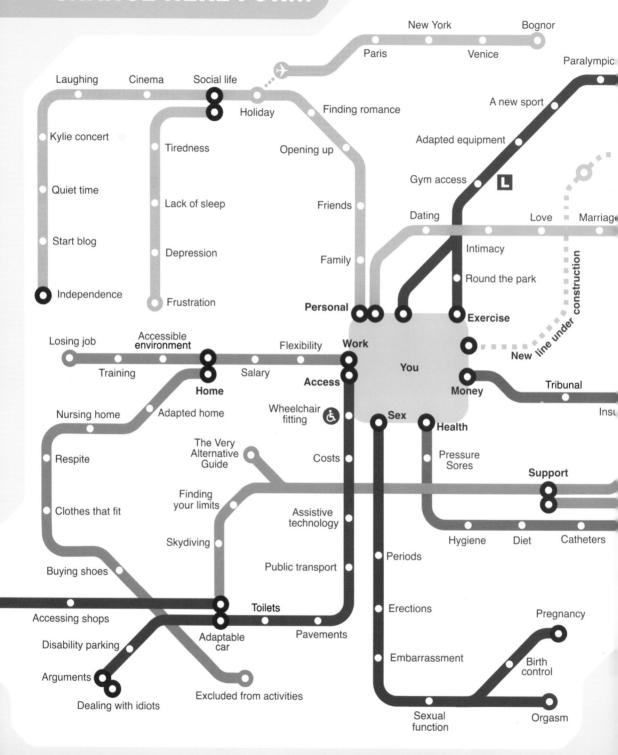

Journey Planner

Personal | Support | Health | Money | Access | Work | Sex | Exercise

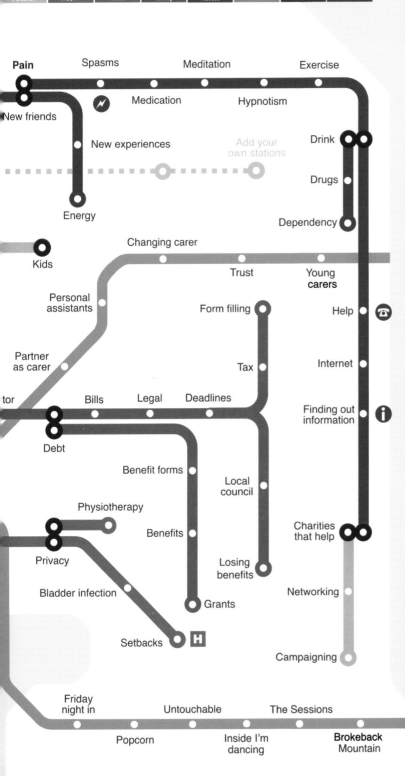

Pain · Spasms · Meditation · Exercise

Medication · Hypnotism

New friends

New experiences · Add your own stations · Drink

Drugs

Energy

Dependency

Changing carer

Kids

Trust · Young carers

Personal assistants

Form filling · Help

Partner as carer

Tax · Internet

...tor · Bills · Legal · Deadlines · Finding out information

Debt

Benefit forms

Local council

Physiotherapy

Benefits

Charities that help

Privacy

Bladder infection · Losing benefits

Grants · Networking

Setbacks · H

Campaigning

Friday night in · Untouchable · The Sessions

Popcorn · Inside I'm dancing · **Brokeback Mountain**

Way out →

Finding your way around life with a spinal injury is hard work. There's so much to think about, it can all feel a bit complicated. You'll wish you just had a bright, clear, colour-coded map that could show you what to do, where to go and how to get there. So here it is!

Well, not quite. Our map simply gives you an idea of some of the things you might come across along your journey. Our lines are fully accessible and if you don't like it at one station, you can always move on to the next. Just don't forget to enjoy the scenery along the way.

If you are unsure which station you need, always ask for advice.

Help Point

Induction Loop Fitted

Skydiving
Push

Cup of tea
Push

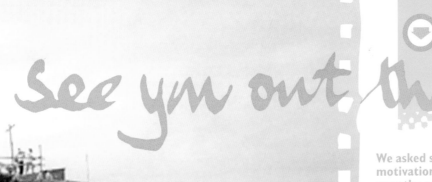

See you out there

We asked someone for a motivational quote to stick near the end of our book. This is what came back...

"My usual rallying cry would be shut up and get on with it - it's better than being a miserable git. Not very politically correct or suitable for a book. It's actually hard to write without sounding all self-righteous and under the influence. So, I'll continue to work on it. By the way, what's the book called?"

THE END

AFTER READING THIS BOOK WE HOPE YOU (OR SOMEONE YOU KNOW) FEELS MORE LIKE THIS...

So how do we end a book like this? With a super-spirited message or a meaningful quote about life? Well, we are concluding it by saying that you've survived a spinal cord injury and that is some serious shit. Fact is, if you can get through that - and still smile - then you can probably get through anything. You might still find it useful to dip back into these pages from time to time, it can be good to look back and see how far you've come.

If the Very Alternative Guide to Spinal Cord Injury has been useful to you, then please let us know. If you really liked it, you may also be interested in the range of mugs, t-shirts, and fluffy toys that will accompany the blockbuster movie when it's inevitably released. Optimistic? Well, as we hope this book has shown, there's nothing wrong with being optimistic.

WEBSITES

There are lots of great web resources available from organisations across the globe. There is also a huge range of personal blogs and forums on spinal injury.

The following is a list of UK organisations and websites we have worked with or found useful.

- Apparelysed
  www.apparalyzed.com
- Aspire
  www.aspire.org.uk
- Back Up
  www.backuptrust.org.uk
- Cauda Equina Syndrome UK Charity
  www.caudaequinauk.com
- Peter Harrison Centre for Disability Sport
  www.lboro.ac.uk/research/phc
- Sexuality and disability
  www.i-said.co.uk
- Spinal Injuries Association
  www.spinal.co.uk
- The Inspire Foundation
  www.inspire-foundation.org.uk
- WheelPower
  www.wheelpower.org.uk

Add your own

IMPORTANT

When to read this book

The best time to read it is during your long and boring rehabilitation process, or later as part of your long and exciting life. Do not read it during the initial moment of injury. If you find someone on the floor who has just suffered a severe spinal injury, please quickly phone for an ambulance rather than giving them this book. Likewise, if you have just suffered a spinal injury and someone gives you this book, try to remain polite but ask them to phone for an ambulance instead.

As a general rule of thumb, during any kind of medical emergency, the preservation of life should take priority over reading popular literature. As good a book as this is there's nothing in here that won't wait until someone comes out of the anaesthetic.

For Aunty Ana, who could always laugh through the toughest of times. AP

To Gopher and Pooks for being there when it counted. JR

Easy On The Eye Books
74 Nethergate
Sheffield S6 6DJ

www.easyontheeyebooks.wordpress.com

First published in Great Britain in 2015

ISBN 978-0-9561439-8-3

© 2015 Anthony Papathomas / Joe Robinson.

Designed in the UK and printed in the EU.

This book was originally funded by Enterprise Project Group at Loughborough University.

The Alternative Guide combines humour and medical information to raise awareness of issues related to spinal injury. Content is based on academic research and personal experience. Although the authors have strived to ensure the accuracy of all material, this book is not intended as professional medical advice.

At the time of printing this first edition is not available in electronic form. We understand that some spinal injured readers may need assistance in reading the book. We are investigating the possibility of an e-book for future editions.

EXCITING GET WELL PUPPY PICTURE PAGE

IS THIS ANOTHER GET WELL GIG?

FOR BOOKWORMS

If you're interested here's a list of our sources.

Causes
• Lee, B. B., Cripps, R. A., Fitzharris, M., & Wing, P. C. (2013). The global map for traumatic spinal cord injury epidemiology: update 2011, global incidence rate. Spinal cord, 52, 110-116.

• National Spinal Cord Injury Statistical Center, Birmingham, Alabama, February, 2012) (https://www.nscisc.uab.edu/PublicDocuments/fact_figures_docs/Facts%202013.pdf)

Anyone Can Join
• Van den Berg, M. E. L., Castellote, J. M., Mahillo-Fernandez, I., & de Pedro-Cuesta, J. (2010). Incidence of spinal cord injury worldwide: a systematic review. Neuroepidemiology, 34, 184-192.

Been There Got the T-shirt
• Kubler-Ross, E., & Kessler, D. A. (2005). On grief and grieving: Finding the meaning of grief through the five stages of loss. Simon and Schuster.

• Clifton, S. (2014). Grieving my broken body: an autoethnographic account of spinal cord injury as an experience of grief. Disability & Rehabilitation, (0), 1-7.

All the quotes
Smith, B., & Sparkes, A. C. (2004). Men, sport, and spinal cord injury: An analysis of metaphors and narrative types. Disability & Society, 19, 613-626.

Smith, B., & Sparkes, A.C. (2005). Men, sport, spinal cord injury, and narratives of hope. Social Science & Medicine, 61, 1095-1105.

Snakes and Ramps
• Sparkes, A. C., & Smith, B. (2005). When narratives matter: men, sport, and spinal cord injury. Medical Humanities, 31, 81-88.

Will I Still Be Able to Do It?
• Baer, R. W. (2003). Is Fred Dead?: A manual on sexuality for men with spinal cord injuries. Dorrance Publishing Company.

• Parker, M. G., & Yau, M. K. (2012). Sexuality, identity and women with spinal cord injury. Sexuality and Disability, 30, 15-27.

Oops I Did It Again
• Lewis, S. J., & Heaton, K. W. (1997). Stool form scale as a useful guide to intestinal transit time. Scandinavian Journal of Gastroenterology, 32, 920-924.

Take It Seriously
• International Review. Pressure ulcer prevention: pressure, shear, friction & micro-climate in context. A consensus document. London: Wounds International, 2010.

Horses for Courses
• Smith, B. Sparkes, A. C. Disability, sport and physical activity. A critical review. In N Watson, A Roulstone, C Thomas, (Eds.), Handbook of Disability Studies (pp. 336-347). Routledge: London: Routledge.

Exercise
• Williams, T., Smith, B., & Papathomas, A. (2014). The barriers, benefits and facilitators of leisure time physical activity among people with spinal cord injury: A meta-synthesis of qualitative findings. Health Psychology Review.

• Smith, B., Papathomas, A., Martin Ginis, K. A., & Latimer-Cheung, A. E. (2013). Understanding physical activity in spinal cord injury rehabilitation: translating and communicating research through stories. Disability & Rehabilitation, 35, 2046-2055. Full physical activity guidelines at: http://sciactioncanada.ca/guidelines/

• Smith, B., & Papathomas, A. (2013). Disability, sport and exercising bodies. In J. Swain, S. French, C. Barnes, & C. Thomas (Eds.), Disabling barriers-Enabling environments (pp. 222-228). London: Sage.

Location, Location, Location
• Smith, B., & Caddick, N. (2013). Research report: Understanding the health and wellbeing of spinal cord injured adults in a care home. (http://www.aspire.org.uk/Data/Sites/1/media/what-we-do/carehomeresearch/carehomeresearchreport.pdf)

• All artwork and photography by Joe Robinson. Puppies and Horse image from 'Animals' Jim Harter (Dover). Mona Lisa public domain image. Lorry photo taken by A.Papathomas.

• Direct quotes were drawn from research conducted by Anthony Papathomas within Loughborough University's Peter Harrison Centre for Disability Sport.

ACKNOWLEDGEMENTS

We thank the Enterprise Project Group at Loughborough University whose funding allowed the original book concept to become a reality.

There are many people who have helped us along the way to writing this book. We would like to offer our thanks to; members of the spinal cord injured community who took the time to attend interviews, helped with feedback sessions on our work and agreed to be photographed.

To the friends and colleagues who have supported us. Professor Vicky Tolfrey and Dr Brett Smith of the Peter Harrison Centre for Disability Sport. Their positivity and expertise in spinal cord injury have been a constant source of encouragement.

Members of our advisor group of experts - Brian Carlin, Helen Smith, Sylvia Coles, Aruna Mahtani, and Mick Magnan - who provided independent feedback on draft work. Also to our copyeditors - Andy Healey and Melissa Papathomas.

To the Aspire Charity for their support in organising focus group sessions and to members of the London Rugby Wheelchair Club and RNOH Stanmore Walkers Group.

Thanks also to; the Coca-Cola Foundation who funded Anthony's employment at Loughborough University at the time this book was written, and our publishers, Easy on the Eye Books, for their passion with this project.

And finally; thanks to the many cafes and coffee shops in and around London and Nottingham for allowing us to reside in their establishments for hours on end without necessarily buying more than coffee and a bit of cake.

AUTHORS

Dr Anthony Papathomas - a research psychologist based within Loughborough University's Peter Harrison Centre for Disability Sport. He has published several articles and book chapters on topics related to disability, and in particular spinal cord injury.

a.papathomas@lboro.ac.uk

Joe Robinson - a freelance artist and designer. Based in London his work covers a wide range of fields including illustration, design, theatre, public art and the unusual creative medium of fire sculpture. He has worked on a range of joint creative academic initiatives.

www.joerobinsonxl.com

Loughborough University

Peter Harrison Centre for Disability Sport

NOTES

NOTES